Making Sense of Fractions

Grades 3-6

Carol Thornton and Judy Wells

ISBN: 1-56911-973-2

Printed in the United States of America.

Table of Contents

Adding and Subtracting Fractions

Multiplying and Dividing Fractions

Introduction

Making Sense of Fractions is designed as a replacement unit to help teachers nurture students' ability to understand and "think mathematically" with fractions. It is important for students to make sense of "the big picture." For this reason, curricular options and related assessment hinge on major fraction constructs.

Making Sense of Fractions is written from a student's perspective. Open-ended tasks need to be embedded in day to day work with fractions. Students' work needs to:

- Challenge them to "think mathematically."
- Encourage them to make choices in relation to their learning.
- Approach learning from different directions and at different levels.
- Approach fractions in ways that make sense to students.

Use literature as a setting for grounding mathematical concepts in everyday situations. The authors suggest *Gator Pie*, published by Sundance Publishing and written by Louise Mathews, as a beginning reference point. This and other books are listed in the bibliography.

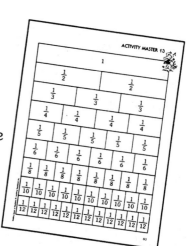

About this Book

Making Sense of Fractions has four major units: fraction concepts, fraction comparisons, equivalences, and the four operations. Teachers may want to place a heavier emphasis on the first two sections with less experienced groups. Students with more experience may move more quickly through these sections for preassessment or review purposes.

All sections begin and end with assessment. On-going assessments are scattered throughout the sessions. The major goals of each session are addressed in *Setting the Stage*. The margin provides a visual reference for needed materials: *Activity Masters* provided in the Appendix, possible student responses, and other relevant information.

While a wide variety of fraction tools are highlighted in various sessions, *Learning Resources' Rainbow Fraction™ Tiles* set is used most often.

The sessions present tasks for a day's work with fractions. The commentary also provides suggested questions and ideas for interpreting, guiding, or understanding students' thinking.

The emphasis in *Making Sense of Fractions* is to help students make important *connections* with fractions. Because students can often help each other accomplish this goal, group work and other forms of collaboration are suggested.

Early Investigations: Understanding Fractions

Setting the Stage: Preassessment

Encourage students to write what they know about fractions.

Students can create a "fraction journal!" Fold four $8\frac{1}{2}$" x 11" pieces of paper in half and staple along the fold.

If students are having difficulty writing about fractions, you might stop and ask if anyone would like to read what they have so far. This allows troubled students to get a start and put something down on paper. If students have little or no knowledge of fractions, tell them it's okay to write "I don't know anything about fractions."

Watch for gaps in understanding as you listen to or read what students have written. Check to see if students:

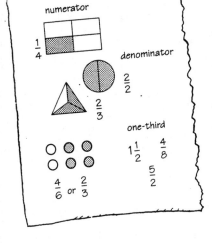

- Create drawings that show "fair shares."
- Use appropriate vocabulary.
- Use only one region model (only circles, only squares...) in their drawings.
- Include any drawings of sets of objects, linear distances, or measures.
- Illustrate contexts for their thinking.
- Use words or symbols when writing fractions.
- Use proper fractions, mixed numbers, or improper fractions.
- Express personal feelings about fractions (easy, hard, important...).

Invite students to share what they'd <u>like</u> to learn about fractions. Their ideas might be recorded in personal journals or in a class journal for future reference!

Making Sense of Fractions © Learning Resources, Inc.

Session 1: Fair Shares

Cut a cake into halves, fourths, eighths, and sixteenths.

Discuss the importance of "fair shares" when slicing a cake. Discuss how the size of each piece changes as the number of pieces increases. As pieces of cake are cut, encourage students to write the fractions being represented. Use appropriate fraction vocabulary.

Review the terms *numerator* and *denominator*. In a cake, the numerator is the number of pieces eaten and the denominator is the number of pieces in the whole cake.

Discuss the following situations:

- What if you start with two cakes?
- What if the number of pieces decreased instead of increased?
- What if the pieces were not the same size?

Encourage students to write a story of their own with fractions!

Session 2: Exploring Fractions Around Us

Look for examples of fractions in the room!

Students might notice, for example:

- $\frac{1}{3}$ of the pencils are sharp.
- $\frac{1}{2}$ of the class wanted hot lunch.
- Clock times can be half and quarter hours.
- $\frac{3}{4}$ of the class is wearing blue.

Ask a group of students to come to the front of the room. Make fraction statements based on observations about students in the group. Students should recognize that if there are three people in the group, all of the fractions will involve thirds. Encourage students to use equivalent fractions to describe the same observation.

Write fractions on the chalkboard as they are identified. Ask students to observe something that could be described as $\frac{0}{4}$ or $\frac{4}{4}$. A fraction for $\frac{4}{4}$ may be that all group members are wearing shoes. Continue this activity, varying the number of students in the group.

Extend your discussion with the following questions.

- Who uses fractions?
- Why do we need fractions?
- Where do we see fractions?

Make statements throughout the day to reinforce students' knowledge of concepts.

- I see that $\frac{3}{4}$ of the groups are ready!
- About half of you have turned in your papers!

Assign students a journal entry for homework. They could write, *"Examples of fractions in my home."* or *"What a day without fractions would be like."*

Making Sense of Fractions © Learning Resources, Inc.

Session 3: The Fraction Box

Preparation: Place a variety of "fraction materials" in a box.*

Invite students to speculate about what might be in the fraction box.

Elicit fractions that can be illustrated by the materials in the fraction box.

- $\frac{1}{3}$ of the color tiles are blue and $\frac{2}{3}$ are red.

- $\frac{1}{2}$ of the cubes are orange and $\frac{2}{4}$ are green.

Encourage students to think of things to add to their fraction boxes. Include a fraction calculator in your fraction box! Show students how to display fractions on the calculator. An overhead calculator is ideal for this initial exploration. Demonstrate fractions as decimals.

Allow students to draw and write about fraction boxes in their fraction journal. The connections between what students "see," "say," and "write" should be made explicit throughout the fraction instruction.

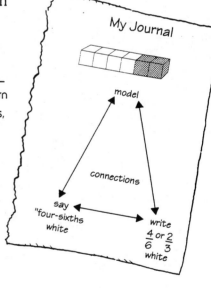

*These materials might include: Rainbow Fraction™ Tiles, color tiles, geoboards, pattern blocks, fraction bars, bean counters, individual candies, loose Unifix® cubes, yarn, rulers, links, measuring cups/spoons, or fraction calculators.

Find Out

Session 4: Fraction Tools

Preparation: Reproduce copies of Activity Masters 1 and 2. Gather a variety of fraction tools such as fraction tiles, geoboards and geobands, colored cubes, color tiles, two-color counters, pattern blocks, and links. Depending on the fraction tools, students may need scissors, crayons, glue, pattern block templates, or paper copies from Activity Masters 3-6.

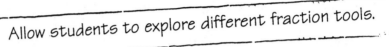

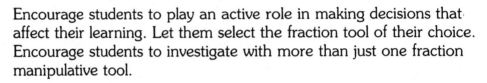

Allow students to explore different fraction tools.

Encourage students to play an active role in making decisions that affect their learning. Let them select the fraction tool of their choice. Encourage students to investigate with more than just one fraction manipulative tool.

Some students will want to model the construction of each fraction. A transparency of Activity Master 2 could be made for this purpose. The basic instructions direct students to:

1. Choose a fraction tool.
2. Pick a number from the Fraction Bank.
3. Use a fraction tool to show your fraction.
4. Sketch your fraction and label it.
5. Use other fraction tools to make the same fraction.
6. Repeat this with another fraction from the bank.

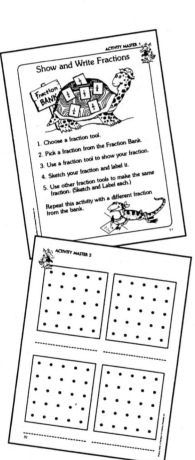

Students' Work

Students can use Activity Master 2 to record their geoboard work. There are several options for recording pattern block work. Students could:

- Trace around a template of pattern block shapes.
- Trace around the actual pattern block.
- Glue matching pieces of construction paper on Activity Masters 3-6.

Most students prefer to draw the tiles, cubes, links, or counters. For these tools, students can change the number of items or their positions to illustrate an equivalent fraction.

Note: The activity directions ask students to look at a model of a fraction and write it. A natural extension is to have students show the written fraction to a classmate and challenge him/her to model it. Students should be allowed to exchange ideas and explain their thought processes.

Making Sense of Fractions © Learning Resources, Inc.

Session 5: Estimating Fractional Parts

Preparation: Duplicate Activity Masters 7 & 8 on contrasting colors of cardstock. Follow the diagram on Activity Master 7 to interlock the circles. You can also use small paper plates of contrasting colors.

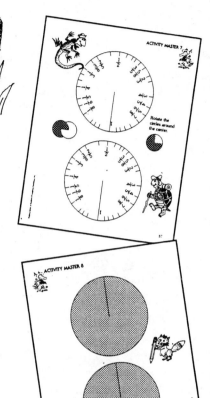

Instruct students to cut out the Activity Master circles. Slide the circles together so that the top half of the circles interlock.

It's important that students overlap their circles the same way so that when the wheel is turned to $\frac{1}{3}$, for example, everyone can describe the fraction using the same color.

Make sure students do not trim circles to make them congruent.

Using paper plates or the unmarked sides of the fraction wheels, ask students to show $\frac{1}{4}$.

Discuss students' strategies for finding $\frac{1}{4}$. Allow time for whole group sharing. Elicit different strategies.

Repeat this exercise for other fractions. Compare the fractions to benchmarks of $\frac{1}{2}$ or $\frac{1}{4}$. Encourage students to tell if their new fractions are greater or less than the benchmarks. Students can take turns calling out new fractions for other students to show.

Using the labeled side of the fraction wheel, encourage students to show fractions as before, then determine fractions for the unlabeled marks.

Listen to students' reasoning about their estimate of the unlabeled marks. Use journals to get a written assessment of students' understandings. Ask them to explain their thinking strategy for the unlabeled marks.

Session 6: Tearing Fractions

Preparation: Provide a 6″ x 9″ envelope and each student will need the same five colors of 9″ x 12″ construction paper.

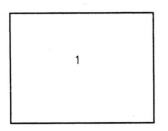

Involve students in making their own fraction kit!

Identify one colored piece of construction paper as the "whole." Label it "1." (Check to see if all students position their paper in the same direction while labeling.)

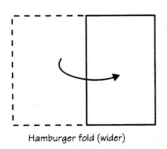
Hamburger fold (wider)

Select a second color to show halves. Instruct students to fold and tear the paper in half. Use a "hamburger" fold, not a "hot dog" fold.

Select, fold, and tear the paper to form fraction pieces for fourths, eighths, and sixteenths. Remind students that each fold should be a "hamburger" fold.

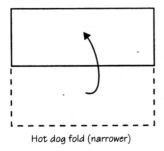
Hot dog fold (narrower)

Ask students to arrange their new pieces so they can cover the whole exactly. Then label all fractions on one side and place students' initials on the other.

Discuss students' discoveries about their pieces. To stimulate pattern finding and generalizations, record students' discoveries in an organized way. Ask students to predict how many pieces there will be for each fraction. Discuss how the denominator gives the answer.

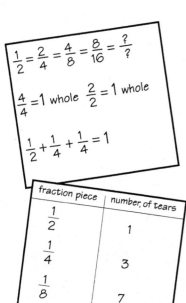

$$\frac{1}{2} = \frac{2}{4} = \frac{4}{8} = \frac{8}{16} = \frac{?}{?}$$

$$\frac{4}{4} = 1 \text{ whole} \quad \frac{2}{2} = 1 \text{ whole}$$

$$\frac{1}{2} + \frac{1}{4} + \frac{1}{4} = 1$$

fraction piece	number of tears
$\frac{1}{2}$	1
$\frac{1}{4}$	3
$\frac{1}{8}$	7
$\frac{1}{16}$	?
$\frac{1}{32}$	?

The Algebra Connection

Challenge students to answer the following questions:

How many tears do you need to do to make the fraction $\frac{1}{2}$, $\frac{1}{4}$, $\frac{1}{8}$...? What patterns do you notice with the denominator and the number of tears?

Keep a chart so that students will notice that the number of tears is one more than twice the previous number of tears or algebraically, "2t + 1," with "t" as the number of tears previously completed. Students may also notice that the number of tears necessary is one less than the denominator. This can be expressed as "d-1" where "d" is the denominator.

Encourage students to count their fraction pieces aloud and write the fraction symbols (e.g. $\frac{1}{4}$, $\frac{2}{4}$, $\frac{3}{4}$, $\frac{4}{4}$...).

Session 7: Fraction Game: What You Spin is What You Take

Preparation: Use fraction game pieces from Session 6, spinners from Activity Master 9A — one for every two students — and a paper clip for each. Also, prepare a spinner for the overhead.

Challenge students to a game where they need to make one whole!

What You Spin Is What You Take

(Use a pencil to anchor the paper clip spinner, as shown.)

1. Spin and place the matching fraction piece on your whole.
2. Keep a running total of what is on each mat.
3. If a player spins and lands on a fraction too large to place on their whole, go on to the next player.
4. The winner is the first to make exactly one whole.

As the game is played, ask questions like:

- Who has more? How much more?
- What would you like to spin next? Why?
- Is it possible for you to win on your next spin?
- What's the probability you will win on your next spin? Is it more likely I'll win on the next spin or you'll win? What's the probability you'll be able to use what you spin?
- What pieces do you need in order to win?
- How much more do you need to win?
- What's the fewest number of spins that would allow you to win?

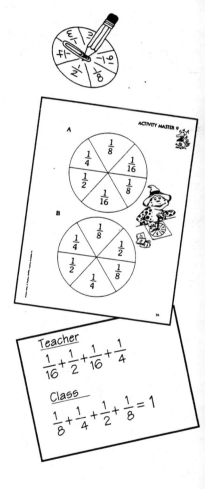

Students will be exposed to the addition of fractions with unlike denominators through play with "What You Spin is What You Take!"

As students become comfortable with the game rules, they should be given the opportunity to play in small groups. Encourage cooperative learning by allowing students to play in teams. You could move two wholes together and change the target number (e.g. to $1\frac{1}{2}$, 2...).

NOTE: Save the fraction pieces for later sessions.

Thirds, Sixths, and Twelfths

Preparation: Give Rainbow Fraction Tiles and Activity Master 10 to students.

Invite students to play a game where the goal is to make a whole using thirds, sixths, and twelfths!

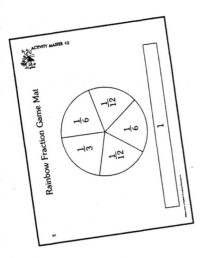

Game rules are the same. The goal is to completely cover the whole on Activity Master 10. As students become comfortable with this version of the game, they might work toward different target numbers using two mats.

14

Session 8: Fair Shares: Problem Solving

Use literature or other themes of interest to pose "fair share" problems for students to model and solve.

It is important to provide a rich variety of problem situations. Some examples are provided below:

- Gordon and Gabriela made a cake and invited six friends. They cut up one whole cake and gave each friend the same amount. Show and write how much cake each friend got.

- Gordon bought a cake from a bakery and shared it with his family. If all four family members ate the same amount, show and write how much <u>three</u> of the relatives ate.

- Five of Gordon's friends shared two granola bars. Show how to divide the granola bars so each friend gets the same amount.

- Three friends were very hungry. They picked up eight granola bars to share. Show how they could divide the bars so each friend would get the same amount.

Each gets $\frac{1}{8}$

Session 9: Fair Shares: Different Shapes, Same Size?

Preparation: Prepare a transparency and copies of Activity Masters 11 and 12. Provide geoboard and geobands, if available.

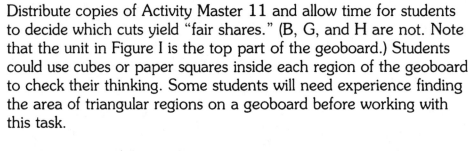

Invite children to examine the "fancy cuts" to decide whether or not there are fair shares.

Distribute copies of Activity Master 11 and allow time for students to decide which cuts yield "fair shares." (B, G, and H are not. Note that the unit in Figure I is the top part of the geoboard.) Students could use cubes or paper squares inside each region of the geoboard to check their thinking. Some students will need experience finding the area of triangular regions on a geoboard before working with this task.

Students should be encouraged to listen critically to their peer's explanations. Alternate reasoning about "fair shares" is an important part of whole class follow-up. Students should conclude that different-shaped regions can be equal shares.

Encourage students to:

- Cut out their favorite "cakes," paste them in their journal, and write reasons to support that the cake shows (or does not show) equal amounts.
- Use Activity Master 12 to allow students to make their own "fancy cuts" in cakes. Let them challenge a friend to determine whether "fair shares" are shown.

Making Sense of Fractions © Learning Resources, Inc.

What Was Learned?

On-going assessment provides insights into students' thinking and guides instructional decision-making on a day to day basis. Teachers can learn about their students' understanding by focusing on a *few big ideas* central to early work with fractions.

For example, do students understand:

- That fractions involve "fair shares" or equal amounts?
- That the more pieces there are in a whole, the smaller each piece is?
- What the numerator and denominator tell about a fraction?
- How to model written fractions and how to write fractions to represent a fraction model or situation?

Open-ended tasks often tell more than anticipated about a learner. They do not limit students' performance. They allow students to be successful at different levels. Specific performance tasks like the following, characterized by open-endedness, might be considered.

Ask students to:

- Choose a fraction tool.
- Represent a fraction.
- Write about it.

Ask students to write about what they see.

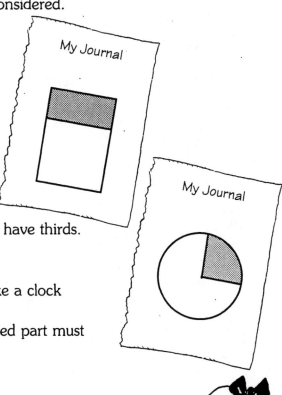

Students might write:

- It's not $\frac{1}{2}$, I can see that. It's less than $\frac{1}{2}$.
- It looks like, if I divided the unshaded part in half, I'd have thirds. I say it's $\frac{1}{3}$!

- That looks like about $\frac{1}{4}$ is shaded, because it looks like a clock at quarter after.
- That's just cut in half and cut in half again. The shaded part must be $\frac{1}{4}$!

These tasks allow us to assess whether students:

- Have exceptional insights and abilities to communicate understanding.
- Satisfactorily communicate understanding of the "big idea(s)" involved.
- Exhibit fragmented understanding(s) or ability to communicate.

Comparisons and Equivalencies

Setting the Stage: Preassessment

Encourage students to write about how Alvin and Alice in the *Gator Pie* story (published by Sundance Publishing) might feel about sharing a pie with more and more visitors. Ask students to explain why Alvin and Alice might have felt this way.

Or

Pretend that Alvin and Alice had more than one pie to share.

- Write fractions to represent what Alvin and Alice should give to each visitor as more arrive.
- Discuss how Alvin and Alice would feel about sharing if there were two pies instead of one. Encourage students to explain their reasoning.

Making Sense of Fractions © Learning Resources, Inc.

Session 1: Rainbow Fractions: Which Is More?

Preparation: Give Rainbow Fraction Tiles to students. Make a transparency of Activity Master 13.

Encourage students to explore relationships among the fraction tiles.

The following questions can guide students to discover important generalizations about comparisons and equivalencies among fractions:

- Tell me what you notice about the tiles.

- Which is greater — $\frac{1}{2}$ or $\frac{1}{3}$? $\frac{1}{3}$ or $\frac{1}{4}$? $\frac{1}{4}$ or $\frac{1}{5}$? $\frac{1}{10}$ or $\frac{1}{12}$? $\frac{1}{12}$ or $\frac{1}{15}$? How did you decide this?

- Which is greater — $\frac{1}{2}$ or $\frac{2}{4}$? $\frac{2}{4}$ or $\frac{3}{6}$? How do you know?

- Which is greater — $\frac{2}{3}$ or $\frac{3}{4}$? $\frac{3}{4}$ or $\frac{4}{5}$? $\frac{4}{5}$ or $\frac{5}{6}$? $\frac{9}{10}$ or $\frac{11}{12}$? $\frac{11}{12}$ or $\frac{14}{15}$? How did you decide this?

Discuss the term *equivalent* with your students.

Direct students to use Rainbow Fraction Tiles in the following *Pick and Compare* activity.

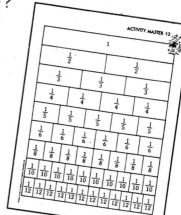

Pick and Compare

1. Arrange students in pairs.
2. Place fraction tiles in a pile.
3. Students pick a tile without peeking.
4. Compare tile with partner.
5. Students make a statement to compare the two tiles.

   "$\frac{1}{8}$ is more than $\frac{1}{10}$."

   "$\frac{1}{10}$ is less than $\frac{1}{8}$."

   Record and keep the tile drawn.

6. If tiles for equivalent fractions are drawn, put them in a discard pile. Continue the activity until all the pieces are drawn.

- Each player must make a "train" of the tiles drawn (excluding tiles for equivalent fractions) in size order.

- Compare the two trains. Encourage students to write statements in their fraction journals about the tiles.

   "My train is almost 2 units long."

   "My train is a little more than $1\frac{1}{2}$."

Session 2: Fraction Tools

Preparation: Reproduce Activity Master 14 and gather fraction tools such as the following: Rainbow Fraction Tiles, pattern blocks, fraction game kit from Early Investigations — Session 6, fraction calculator...

Students work with a partner to brainstorm and record observations as they compare fractions or show equivalence.

Students need to explore fractional relationships with several tools to stimulate and develop thinking about fractions. Since fraction tools are based on the same concept, it doesn't matter which tool is selected first. Encourage students to explore all available tools. Some students may be ready to explore equivalent fractions on the calculator. Provide assistance with this learning activity.

1. Choose a fraction tool.
2. Demonstrate two fractions with the tool.
3. Make statements to compare fractions or show equivalence.
4. Draw a sketch and label it.

   Repeat the steps for other fractions.

Provide time for students to compare their ideas with other groups before sharing with the whole class. Record students' findings on the board so that comparison or equivalent relationships can be highlighted.

If students have not noticed the relationship between numerators and denominators of equivalent fractions, ask them to study the data and comment on any patterns they notice. Students may say: "When the numerator doubles, so does the denominator."

Or

Teach students to develop estimating skills by comparing fractions to benchmarks. For example, "$\frac{3}{4}$ is more than $\frac{3}{8}$, because $\frac{3}{4}$ is more than $\frac{1}{2}$ and $\frac{3}{8}$ is less than $\frac{1}{2}$. These fractions have the same numerator but, since fourths are bigger than eighths, $\frac{3}{4}$ has to be bigger than $\frac{3}{8}$."

A bulletin board or hallway display could be made of students' work.

Making Sense of Fractions © Learning Resources, Inc.

Session 3: Fraction Game: What You Spin Is What You Take

Preparation: Give fraction game pieces made in Early Investigations — Session 6 and spinners (Activity Master 9) to students. Make a transparency of Activity Master 9 for overhead use.

Invite students to revisit an old game with a new twist!

Students will develop their concept of equivalence through trades for the same fraction color.

What You Spin Is What You Take

Spin to see who goes first. (Use a pencil to anchor the paper clip spinner, as shown.)

1. Spin and place the matching fraction piece on the whole.
2. Check to see if all your pieces are the same **color**. If not, trade for equivalent pieces.
3. Record what is on each mat for each turn.
4. If a player spins and lands on a piece that is too big to fit on the mat, go to the next player.

The winner is the first player to make exactly one whole.

Players will need to change colors several times during game play until sixteenths are placed on the board. Ask the following questions to stimulate thinking during game play:

- Who has more? How much more?
- What would you like to spin next? Why?
- Is it possible for you to win on your next spin?
- Do you think you might have to change colors on your next turn?
- What's the probability you will win on your next spin? Is it more likely I'll win on the next spin or you'll win? What's the probability you'll be able to use what you spin?
- What pieces do you need in order to win?
- How much more do you need to win?
- What's the fewest number of spins that would allow you to win?

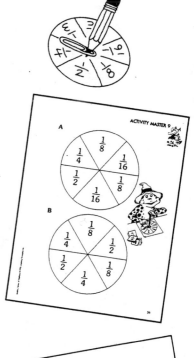

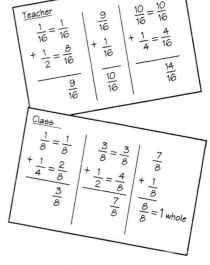

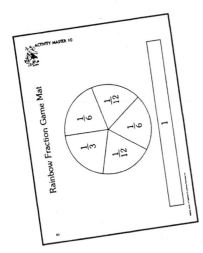

As students become comfortable with the game rules, they should be given the opportunity to play in small groups. Encourage cooperative learning, by allowing students to play in teams.

Move two wholes together and change the target number to vary the game.

Thirds, Sixths, and Twelfths

Preparation: Give Rainbow Fraction Tiles and Activity Master 10 to students.

Invite students to play a game where the goal is to make a whole using thirds, sixths, and twelfths!

Game rules are the same. The goal is to completely cover the whole on Activity Master 10. As students become comfortable with this version of the game, they might work toward different target numbers using two mats.

Making Sense of Fractions © Learning Resources, Inc.

Session 4: Fraction Game: Which Is Less? Which Is More?

Preparation: *Provide Rainbow Fraction Tiles, Activity Master 15, and Activity Master 16 for each pair of students.*

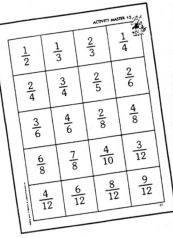

Engage students in a partner game where they can compare fractions!

Which Is Less? Which Is More?

Mix the cards and put them face down in a pile.

1. Each player picks one fraction card.
2. If equivalent fractions are drawn, players keep their cards.
3. Spin the spinner. Make a statement about the two fractions using the word from the spinner.
4. The spinner determines who takes both cards — the one with the lesser or greater fraction.

Continue until all cards are gone. Spin one more time. The player who has more or less according to the spinner is the winner!

Session 5: Comparison Problems

Preparation: Provide Rainbow Fraction Tiles for students.

Invite children to use Rainbow Fraction Tiles to model, solve, and record problems!

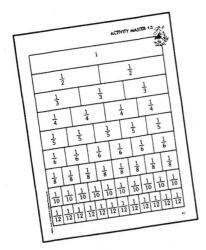

It is important to provide a rich variety of problems for the comparison of fractions. Some examples are provided below.

- One week Gloria and Gerald tried to walk every day. They kept a chart of their distance each day.

Our Daily Walk

	Gloria	Gerald
Monday	$\frac{1}{4}$ of a mile	$\frac{3}{12}$ of a mile
Tuesday	$\frac{1}{3}$ of a mile	$\frac{5}{12}$ of a mile
Wednesday	$\frac{2}{3}$ of a mile	$\frac{8}{12}$ of a mile
Thursday	$\frac{3}{4}$ of a mile	$\frac{7}{12}$ of a mile
Friday	$\frac{2}{5}$ of a mile	$\frac{1}{2}$ of a mile
Saturday	$\frac{2}{3}$ of a mile	$\frac{3}{4}$ of a mile

Decide whether Gloria walked more, less, or the same distance as Gerald each day. Who walked more over the week? How many miles did Gerald and Gloria walk together each day? What was their week's total?

- On Sunday Gloria and Gerald decided to have a picnic with friends. They sat at two picnic tables. There was one big pizza for each table. At Gerald's table three friends shared the pizza equally. At Gloria's table the pizza was shared equally among four. Who got more pizza?

24

Making Sense of Fractions © Learning Resources, Inc.

Session 6: Counting and Equivalencies

Preparation: Provide Rainbow Fraction Tiles for students.

Involve students in counting fractions beyond one!

Counting Mixed Numbers

Ask students to stand. Group them in fours. Signal to the first student to sit. Continue counting by fourths "$\frac{1}{4}, \frac{2}{4}, \frac{3}{4}, \frac{4}{4}$..." until one group of students is seated. Count the second group by writing 1 , $\frac{1}{4}$ $1\frac{2}{4}$... until the whole class is seated.

Repeat this process for thirds and fifths.

Counting Improper Fractions

Place six $\frac{1}{4}$ tiles on a desk and count by fourths only (e.g. $\frac{1}{4}, \frac{2}{4}, \frac{3}{4}, \frac{4}{4}, \frac{5}{4}, \frac{6}{4}$...) as each tile is picked up by students. Describe this arrangement in at least two ways. Typical student responses appear in the sample box.

This situation explores the relationship between mixed numbers and improper fractions. Introduce appropriate terminology. Repeat this process to develop concepts for finding equivalent mixed numbers and improper fractions.

> Typical student responses:
>
> • I see $\frac{6}{4}$.
>
> • I see 1 and $\frac{2}{4}$.
>
> • That's the same as $1\frac{1}{2}$.

Mixed Numbers and Improper Fractions

Make a list of equivalencies between improper fractions and mixed numbers. As students examine the list and compare counting patterns, they will begin to see patterns in ways that make sense to them. Examples may include:

- Dividing (when changing from improper fractions to mixed numbers).
- Multiplying (when changing from mixed numbers to improper fractions).

Encourage students to find equivalencies between improper fractions and mixed numbers. Give fraction tools for exploration. Students should record these equivalencies and any generalizations they observe in their fraction journals.

Session 7: Walking You Home

Preparation: Hang a clothesline in the classroom.
Distribute one fraction card from Activity Masters 15 and 17 to each student. Clip "0" and "4" to the line. Make Rainbow Fraction Tiles available for students' reference.

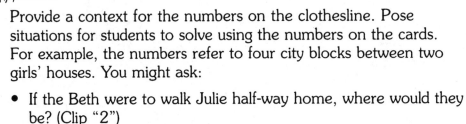

Ask students to order fractions on a clothesline and explain their thinking!

Provide a context for the numbers on the clothesline. Pose situations for students to solve using the numbers on the cards. For example, the numbers refer to four city blocks between two girls' houses. You might ask:

- If the Beth were to walk Julie half-way home, where would they be? (Clip "2")
- If Julie then walked Beth half-way to her home, where would they be? (Clip "1")

Then clip the "3" and have students place their clothespins on the line.

Allow students to examine the completed line, to agree or disagree with placements, and to verbalize their reasoning. Encourage students to use Rainbow Fraction Tiles to help or check their theories.

Students should only be allowed to change the placement of a clothespin if they can justify their reason for doing so.

Extensions:

- Students should be encouraged to label and place additional clothespins on the line.
- Students can state a fraction that is not already displayed and ask classmates to approximate its placement.
- During discussion, elicit examples of ordered lines in real life (e.g. ruler, mile markers, markers for a cross-country run, timelines, etc.).

Making Sense of Fractions © Learning Resources, Inc.

Session 8: Fraction Riddles and Problems

(Revisiting Concepts, Comparisons, and Equivalencies)

Preparation: Provide Rainbow Fraction Tiles for students.

Pose problems and riddles for students to solve. Challenge students to find as many solutions as possible or to create their own riddles for others to solve!

Sample Riddles

I have five tiles equal to $1\frac{1}{2}$. What could they be?
Sample solutions: $\frac{1}{4}, \frac{1}{4}, \frac{1}{4}, \frac{1}{4}, \frac{1}{2}$ or $\frac{1}{8}, \frac{1}{8}, \frac{1}{4}, \frac{1}{2}, \frac{1}{2}$

I have seven tiles equal to one whole bar. What could they be?
Sample solutions:

$\frac{1}{6}, \frac{1}{3}, \frac{1}{6}, \frac{1}{12}, \frac{1}{12}, \frac{1}{12}, \frac{1}{12}$ or $\frac{1}{6}, \frac{1}{6}, \frac{1}{6}, \frac{1}{6}, \frac{1}{6}, \frac{1}{12}, \frac{1}{12}$

I have five tiles equal to $\frac{7}{6}$. What could they be?
Sample solutions: $\frac{1}{6}, \frac{1}{6}, \frac{1}{3}, \frac{1}{4}, \frac{1}{4}$ or $\frac{1}{6}, \frac{1}{6}, \frac{1}{6}, \frac{1}{6}, \frac{1}{2}$

Problem Task 1

Complete Activity Sheet 18.

Problem Task 2

Complete Activity Sheet 19. Encourage students to make other slices.

Problem Task 3

Complete Activity Sheet 20.

Problem Task 4

Write fractions on self-adhesive labels and place them on students' backs. Students have to determine the fraction that is on their back by asking classmates questions that can only be answered by "yes" or "no." Challenge students to order themselves from least to greatest.

Encourage students to share questions that gave them the most information.

What Was Learned?

Focus on "big ideas" with comparisons and equivalencies to gain additional insights into students' understandings of fractions.

For example, do students recognize:

- That fractional numbers have many equivalent names/forms?
- That fractions that represent the same amount can be written as a mixed number or an improper fraction?
- That some "nice" numbers (e.g., 0, $\frac{1}{2}$, 1...) provide valuable benchmarks for estimating comparisons?
- That a constant relationship between numerators and denominators will yield equivalent fractions?

Open-ended tasks like the following may address many of these ideas.

Sample Task 1

Students might be asked to:

1. Select two fractions.
2. Sketch or model each with a fraction tool.
3. Write about the relationship between the two fractions.

Sample Task 2

Preparation: Keeping the perforated edge intact, cut computer paper lengthwise so that 2-3 pages of paper (still attached) can be given to each student.

Write approximately fifteen fractions from Activity Masters 15 and 17 on the chalkboard.

Ask students to:

1. Use a ruler to draw a fraction line.
2. Choose ten fractions from the chalkboard and place them on the number line.

Making Sense of Fractions © Learning Resources, Inc.

Adding and Subtracting Fractions

Setting the Stage: Preassessment

Preparation: Gather a variety of fraction tools for students' use. You will need an overhead fraction calculator for teacher use.

Students will examine the result of addition and subtraction fraction problems.

Marla wanted to swim across the pond. She swam $\frac{1}{3}$ of the way across but then was tired. She drifted back as she floated and rested. When she woke up, she swam half way across and rested again. If Marla had continued to swim instead of resting and drifting back, would she have made it all the way across? Add $\frac{1}{3}$ and $\frac{1}{2}$.

Watch students as they try to solve the problem.

$\frac{1}{3}$	$\frac{1}{2}$

$$\frac{1}{3} = \frac{2}{6}$$
$$+ \frac{1}{2} = \frac{3}{6}$$
$$\overline{ \frac{5}{6}}$$

$\frac{1}{6}$	$\frac{1}{6}$	$\frac{1}{6}$	$\frac{1}{6}$	$\frac{1}{6}$

- Do they use the fraction tiles to model the problem?
- Do they use a paper and pencil approach?
- Do they carry out mental calculations?
- Do they use some combination of the above?

Encourage students to use a calculator to solve the problems. Watch as they enter keystrokes.

- Do students approach the problem by adding then subtracting?
- Do they use the memory function?
- Do they add and recognize that the result is less than one?
- Do they start with the whole and subtract?

Encourage students to communicate their thinking in meaningful ways. As you observe and listen to students, try to characterize the level and nature of their responses. This is the basis for subsequent planning and instruction.

Session 1: Problem Solving

Preparation: Make Rainbow Fraction Tiles available to students.

Create addition/subtraction problems for students to model, solve, and record!

Include all types of addition and subtraction problem situations:

1. Put together. ($\frac{1}{4} + \frac{1}{4} = n$)
2. Take away. ($\frac{1}{2} - \frac{1}{4} = n$)
3. How much more is needed? ($\frac{1}{3} + n = \frac{1}{2}$)
4. How much was taken away? ($\frac{3}{4} - n = \frac{1}{4}$)
5. Comparison (How much more is __ than__?)
6. Comparison (How much less is__than__?)
7. How much at the beginning, before adding some? ($n + \frac{1}{4} = \frac{1}{2}$)
8. How much at the beginning before subtracting? ($n - \frac{1}{8} = \frac{1}{4}$)
9. How much was taken away? ($\frac{3}{4} - n = \frac{1}{4}$)
10. Know the whole, know the part, find the other part.
    ($\frac{1}{2} = \frac{1}{4} + n$)

Some examples are provided below. Students should:

- Listen to the problem situation.
- Represent the situation with fraction tools.
- Record in a meaningful way.

Different approaches should be expected and encouraged, as some situations can be correctly represented as either addition or subtraction. Allow adequate time for students to present and discuss various approaches. Include multi-step problems.

Sample Problem Situations

- Seth had a quart bucket that was $\frac{3}{4}$ full of berries. He gave $\frac{1}{2}$ quart to Lindy and ate the rest. How much of the quart did he eat?
- Seth ate $\frac{1}{2}$ of a pie. Lindy ate $\frac{2}{3}$ of a pie. How much more did Lindy eat than Seth?

Encourage students to create their own problems for classmates to solve.

Making Sense of Fractions © Learning Resources, Inc.

Session 2: In Order

Preparation: Use Activity Masters 15 and 17 to prepare a deck of fraction cards. Omit the improper fractions. Hang a clothesline in the classroom and clip 0, 1, 2, 3, and 4 to it. Make Rainbow Fraction Tiles available for students to use.

Students will estimate and sequence sums and differences!

Whole-Class Introduction

Ask a pair of students to:

• Pick two cards from the deck.
• Agree on an estimate of the sum.

Write the sum on a paper square and let students pin it to the clothesline in sequence.

Allow students to examine the sum and its placement. Students should agree or disagree and verbalize their reasoning.

Repeat the activity asking for sums or differences. Students could be challenged:

• To create their own problem situation to match given fraction pairs.
• To pick three fraction cards and estimate the sum.
• To create fractions that, when added or subtracted, fall in a given range.
• To suggest fractions whose sum is about twice as much as one just displayed.

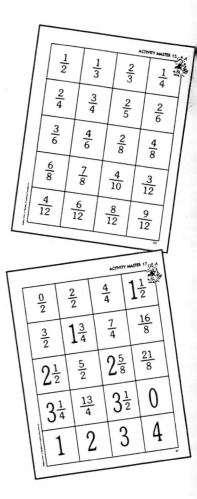

ACTIVITY MASTER 15

$\frac{1}{2}$	$\frac{1}{3}$	$\frac{2}{3}$	$\frac{1}{4}$
$\frac{2}{4}$	$\frac{3}{4}$	$\frac{2}{5}$	$\frac{2}{6}$
$\frac{3}{6}$	$\frac{4}{6}$	$\frac{2}{8}$	$\frac{4}{8}$
$\frac{6}{8}$	$\frac{7}{8}$	$\frac{4}{10}$	$\frac{3}{12}$
$\frac{4}{12}$	$\frac{6}{12}$	$\frac{8}{12}$	$\frac{9}{12}$

ACTIVITY MASTER 17

$\frac{0}{2}$	$\frac{2}{2}$	$\frac{4}{4}$	$1\frac{1}{2}$
$\frac{3}{2}$	$1\frac{3}{4}$	$\frac{7}{4}$	$\frac{16}{8}$
$2\frac{1}{2}$	$\frac{5}{2}$	$2\frac{5}{8}$	$\frac{21}{8}$
$3\frac{1}{4}$	$\frac{13}{4}$	$3\frac{1}{2}$	0
1	2	3	4

Session 3: Fraction Game:
What You Spin Is What You Take/Take Away

Preparation: Provide fraction game pieces made in Early Investigations — Session 6, spinners from Activity Master 9-A, and an overhead transparency of spinners. Use Activity Master 21 for reference.

Invite students to revisit an old game with a new twist!

What You Spin is What You Take

Play several rounds of Session 7 — Early Investigation's version of the game. Encourage students to show fraction equivalences as they record them.

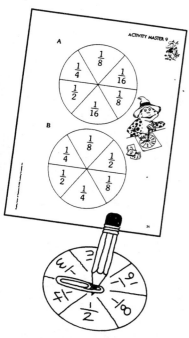

What You Spin is What You Take Away

Game directions are similar to previous sessions. Players now start with one whole and take away a fraction. The goal is to be the first to remove all the fraction pieces. The last fraction piece must exactly match the remaining fraction on the spinner. Game directions follow:

Spin to see who goes first. (Use a pencil to anchor the paper clip spinner, as shown.)

1. Start with the whole piece.
2. Spin and take the matching fraction piece away, making trades as needed.
3. If there is not enough left to take what is on the spinner, the next player gets a turn.
4. Keep track of what is on your mat.
5. The winner is the first to remove all fraction pieces!

Ask questions to stimulate thinking during game play:

- Who has more? How much more?
- What would you like to spin next? Why?
- Is it possible for you to win on your next spin?
- What's the probability you will win on your next spin? Is it more likely I'll win on the next spin or you'll win? What's the probability you'll be able to use what you spin?
- What's the fewest number of spins that would allow you to win?

32

As students become comfortable with the game rules, they should be given the opportunity to play in small groups. Encourage cooperative learning by allowing students to play in teams.

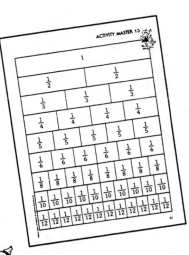

Move two wholes together and change the starting number to vary the game (e.g. to $1\frac{1}{2}$, to 2...).

Thirds, Sixths, and Twelfths

Preparation: Provide Rainbow Fraction Tiles and Activity Master 10 for each pair of students.

Invite students to play a game where the goal is to start with a whole and take off thirds, sixths, and twelfths.

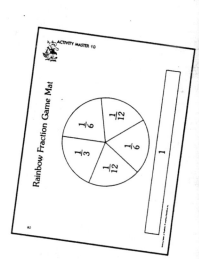

Game rules are the same as before. The goal is to completely remove the tiles. As students become comfortable with this version of the game, they might start with different target numbers (e.g. $1\frac{3}{4}$, 2...).

After each game, revisit one move to show different aspects of recording. Ask students to find different ways to approach recording (e.g. using common denominators, equivalent fractions ...).

Session 4: Menu Options

Preparation: Make a transparency of Activity Master 22. Provide Rainbow Fraction Tiles and spinners. Use two copies of Activity Master 15 to make a game deck for each pair of students. Use Activity Masters 23, 24, and 25 for Close To, Two and Two, and Pick 4. Use Activity Master 21 for What You Spin Is What You Take/Away.

Students will choose from a menu and work in teams.

Menu tasks are designed for partner work. The menu allows students to become flexible in their thinking about adding and subtracting fractions. Allow sufficient time for students to sample all the menu tasks. Create extra sets of menu materials so groups of students can work on one menu task simultaneously.

Menu Choices

Close To...

Players pick two cards, then estimate whether the sum is closer to 0, $\frac{1}{2}$, 1, $1\frac{1}{2}$, or 2. They place the cards over that number on the mat. Partners use fraction pieces or a calculator to check. Players keep the cards if they are correct. If not, they forfeit the cards to their partner.

Two and Two.

Each player picks two cards. They must add or subtract the fractions and record the results. On the subtraction round, the player with the smaller result tallies one point. On the addition round, the player with the greater result tallies one point. Use fraction tools to help or check. Game ends at ten points.

Pick 4.

Draw four cards. Use as many as needed to show a sum that is greater than $\frac{1}{2}$ but less than $1\frac{1}{2}$. Record your answer. Use fraction tools to help or check.

You can change the target numbers and provide additional fraction cards as needed to alter each game.

What You Spin is What You Take/Away.

These menu selections provide additional exposure to familiar, "powerful" games. Directions are provided on Activity Master 21.

Making Sense of Fractions © Learning Resources, Inc.

Session 5: Calculator Target

Preparation: Provide fraction calculators and an overhead calculator for introducing this session. (The directions below are based on the student CALC-U-VUE® from Learning Resources® and the TI-12 Math Explorer. (Modification may be needed for other brands.)

Involve students in a calculator game which requires them to add or subtract fractions mentally.

TI-12 Math Explorer:

1. Clear the memory.
2. Select a target number. (e.g. $2\frac{1}{4}$)
3. Enter a proper fraction and press $\boxed{m+}$.
   (e.g. $\boxed{1}$ $\boxed{/}$ $\boxed{8}$ $\boxed{=}$ $\boxed{m+}$)
4. Mentally calculate what is in memory.
5. Continue pressing $\boxed{m+}$ until you think the target number is in the memory.
6. Press $\boxed{mr}$ to check! (You need to press $\boxed{m+}$ eighteen times with the fraction $\frac{1}{8}$ to get $2\frac{1}{4}$.)

Press $\boxed{Ab/c}$ or $\boxed{Simp}$ on the TI-12 Math Explorer for added assistance while simplifying fractions.

Some students may need assistance in changing an improper fraction on the display to a mixed number. Provide opportunities for students to share their strategies.

As students become comfortable with the task, allow time for them to work in pairs.

Variation:

- Enter a number and successively subtract until zero, the *target number,* is reached.
- Starting with a known number, partners in turn could secretly add/subtract, show the result, and challenge the other to determine what was done to obtain that result.

Guess My Rule

- One player decides on a rule (e.g. add $\frac{1}{2}$) and enters $\boxed{1}\ \boxed{/}\ \boxed{2}\ \boxed{=}\ \boxed{M+}$ into the calculator.
- This player then hides the number being added by pressing any other fraction.
- Partner tries to guess the rule by entering any fraction and pressing $\boxed{=}$.
- Continue entering fractions and pressing $\boxed{=}$ until the rule can be stated.

Keep score of the numbers of attempts needed to determine the rules.

Making Sense of Fractions © Learning Resources, Inc.

Session 6: Fraction Problems and Riddles

Preparation: Provide Fraction Tiles and transparencies of Activity Masters 15 and 26.

Pose problems and riddles for students to solve and challenge students to find as many different solutions as they can and to create their own for others to solve!

Sample Riddles

I have two cards. Their sum is more than one but less than $1\frac{1}{2}$. What could they be? Explain your reasoning.
Sample solutions: $\frac{2}{3} + \frac{3}{4}$ or $\frac{7}{8} + \frac{4}{10}$

I have two cards. Their sum is more than $\frac{1}{2}$ but less than one. What could they be?
Sample solutions: $\frac{1}{2} + \frac{1}{3}$ or $\frac{2}{3} + \frac{1}{4}$

I have two cards. Their difference is less than $\frac{1}{2}$. What could they be?
Sample solutions: $\frac{7}{8} - \frac{3}{4}$ or $\frac{9}{12} - \frac{1}{6}$

Students can work in pairs to solve the problems below, record their solutions, and share them in a class discussion.

Problem Task 1

1. Secretly pick two fractions from Activity Master 15 and add or subtract them.
2. Tell your partner the answer.
3. Your partner tells you what the problem could have been!

As a variation, pick and then tell your partner one fraction from Activity Master 15. Your partner has to think of a fraction whose sum or difference is that fraction. Use fraction tools to help or check.

Problem Task 2

1. Each partner copies the fraction mat on their own paper.
2. Spin and choose where to write the number on the mat. Use fraction tools to help or check. Repeat. Fill each box with a different number.

Change to subtraction or change the target number for variations.

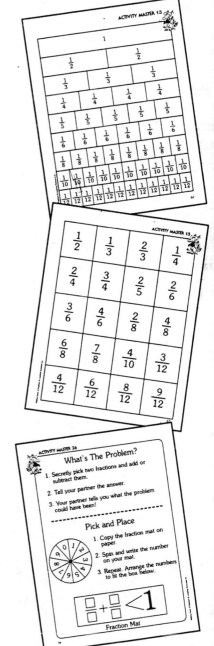

Making Sense of Fractions © Learning Resources, Inc.

What Was Learned?

Focus on "big ideas" for addition and subtraction concepts. This will provide further perspectives about students' understandings of fractions.

Teachers may be interested in whether students:
• Have enough number sense to make good estimations for sums and differences.
• Combine like units when they add or subtract.
• Recognize equivalent ways of expressing results.
• Can determine whether a resulting sum or difference is a reasonable one.

Open-ended tasks may address many of these "big ideas."

Sample Task

Use Activity Master 15 and ask students to:

• Pick any two fractions and add them.
• Think: How much more or less than $1\frac{1}{2}$ is the sum?
• Explain how they made their decisions.

   NOTE: Students may use a variety of methods to help or check their thinking for this task:

• Estimation
• Rainbow Fraction Tiles
• Calculator or other fraction tools.
• Written computation

Making Sense of Fractions © Learning Resources, Inc.

Multiplying and Dividing Fractions

Setting the Stage: Preassessment

Preparation: Provide variety of fraction tools for students to use.

Encourage students to solve problems which involve the multiplication or division of fractions.

Introduce the multiplication and division of fractions with literature! The authors suggest *Gator Pie* or other literature to provide a context for fraction work.

Multiplication

Ask your students to pretend that in the *Gator Pie* story that there were eighteen alligators near Alvin and twelve near Alice. One-third of the total number of alligators near Alvin had hats and $\frac{3}{4}$ of those near Alice had hats. How many total alligators were wearing hats?

Division

Ask your students to pretend that in the *Gator Pie* story that Alvin had six sandwiches and Alice had nine. Alvin cut his sandwiches in thirds. Alice cut hers in fourths. How many sandwich pieces were there in all?

Pose problems and observe the methods students use to follow them. Do students:

- Recognize the problem as multiplication or division?
- Solve the problem in an informal way?
- Use diagrams to represent and solve the problem?
- Use fraction tools?
- Prefer a paper-pencil approach?
- Carry out mental calculations?
- Use some combination of the above?

Encourage students to communicate their thinking in meaningful ways. Observe and listen to students to characterize the level and nature of their responses. This is the basis for subsequent planning and instruction.

Session 1: Problem Solving

Preparation: Make Rainbow Fraction Tiles available to students.

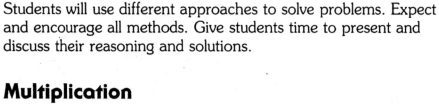
Encourage students to model, solve, and record problems in a meaningful way. Create multiplication/division problems for students to model, solve, and record!

Students should:

- Listen to the problem situation.
- Represent the situation with materials, drawings, and numbers.
- Record their results.

Students will use different approaches to solve problems. Expect and encourage all methods. Give students time to present and discuss their reasoning and solutions.

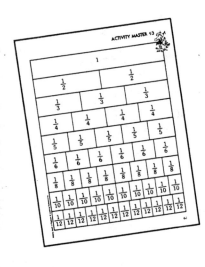

Multiplication

- $\frac{1}{3}$ of the frogs who came to the frog picnic wore sunglasses. Twelve frogs attended the picnic. How many wore sunglasses?
- Stephen noted that $\frac{3}{4}$ of the twelve frogs were wearing hats. How many were wearing hats?

Division

- Frank had three pizzas. He wanted each gator to have $\frac{1}{4}$ of a pizza. How many friends could eat pizza with Frank's plan?
- Heidi had six cakes for dessert. She put $\frac{2}{3}$ of a cake on each plate until all the cake was gone. How many plates of cake did she have?
- Heidi had four granola bars. She put $\frac{3}{4}$ of a bar on each plate. How many plates had granola bars on them?

Encourage students to create their own problems for classmates to solve.

40

Making Sense of Fractions © Learning Resources, Inc.

Session 2: Fraction Game: Take Half of What You Spin

Preparation: Provide fraction game pieces from Early Investigations — Session 6, spinners from Activity Master 9, and a transparency of spinners for overhead use.

Invite students to revisit an old game with a new twist!

Take Half of What You Spin

Spin to see who goes first. (Use a pencil to anchor the paper clip spinner, as shown.)

1. Spin and place fractions on the whole for half of what the spinner says.
2. Record what is on each mat.
3. If a player spins and lands on a piece that is too big to fit on their mat, go to the next player.

The winner is the first player to make exactly a whole.

Ask questions like:

- Who has more? How much more?
- Is it possible for you to win on your next spin?
- What's the probability you will win on your next spin? Is it more likely I'll win on the next spin or you'll win? What's the probability you'll be able to use what you spin?
- What pieces do you need in order to win?
- How much more do you need to win?
- What's the fewest number of spins that would allow you to win?

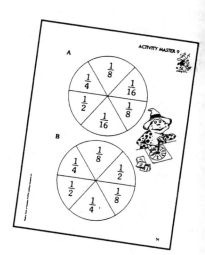

As students become comfortable with the game rules, they should be given the opportunity to play in small groups. Encourage cooperative learning by allowing students to play as teams.

Move two wholes together and change the target number (e.g. to $1\frac{1}{2}$, 2...).

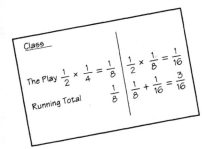

About Recording

For students to record number sentence, it might help to highlight the parallel between:

Two groups of four – (written as 2 x 4) and two groups of half – (written as $2 \times \frac{1}{2}$).

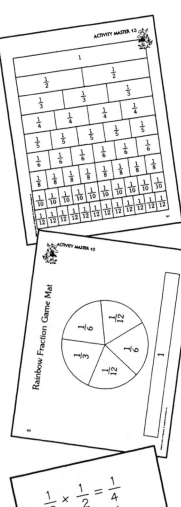

Take Half of Thirds or Sixths

Preparation: Give Rainbow Fraction Tiles and Activity Master 10 to students. Before reproducing the mat, replace the " $\frac{1}{12}$ s " with $\frac{1}{3}$ and $\frac{1}{6}$.

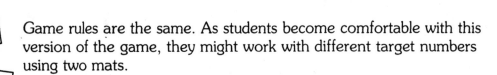

Invite students to play a game where they take half of thirds and sixths to make a whole!

Game rules are the same. As students become comfortable with this version of the game, they might work with different target numbers using two mats.

Encourage students to examine patterns in numbers (i.e., multiplying numerators, multiplying denominators).

$$\frac{1}{2} \times \frac{1}{2} = \frac{1}{4}$$
$$\frac{1}{2} \times \frac{1}{8} = \frac{1}{16}$$
$$\frac{1}{2} \times \frac{1}{4} = \frac{1}{8}$$

42

Making Sense of Fractions © Learning Resources, Inc.

Session 3: Fraction Game: About How Many?

Preparation: Gather fraction game pieces made in Early Investigations — Session 6, spinners from Activity Master 9A and a transparency of spinners for overhead use.

Invite students to revisit an old game with a new twist!

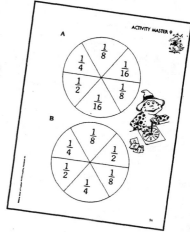

About How Many?

Spin to see who goes first. (Use a pencil to anchor the paper clip spinner, as shown.)

1. Fill the whole part way with fraction pieces.
2. Spin and tell about how many fraction pieces (for the spinner) would exactly cover what's on the mat.
3. Record a description of the situation.

Each time a player makes a list that is verified by their opponent, they earn one point. Play ends at ten points.

Example:

Fill $\frac{3}{4}$ of the mat.
- If the spinner lands on $\frac{1}{2}$, then $1\frac{1}{2}$ would fit.
- If the spinner lands on $\frac{1}{4}$, then 3 would fit.

To record, it might help to highlight the parallel between:
$8 \div 2$ — thought of as, "How many two's are in eight?"

As students become comfortable with the game rules, they should be given the opportunity to play in small groups. Encourage cooperative learning by allowing students to play as teams.

Move two wholes together and change the target number to vary the game.

Session 4: In Order

Preparation: Use Activity Masters 15 and 17 (omit improper fractions) to prepare a deck of fraction cards. Hang a clothesline in the classroom and clip 0, 1, 2, 3, and 4 to it.

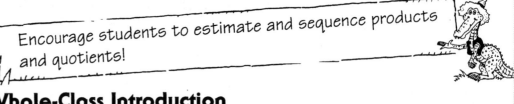

Encourage students to estimate and sequence products and quotients!

Whole-Class Introduction

Introduce the activity by asking a pair of students to:

- Pick two cards from the deck.
- Agree on an estimate of the product.
- Write the product on a paper square.
- Pin the square in sequence on the line.

Allow students to examine the estimated product and its placement, to agree or disagree, and to verbalize their reasoning. Students can only change a card placement if they can justify their reason for doing so.

Repeat the activity asking for products or quotients. Challenge students:

- To create their own problem situation to match given fraction pairs.
- To create fractions that, when multiplied or divided, fall in a given range (e.g., between $1\frac{1}{3}$ and $1\frac{1}{2}$).
- To suggest fractions whose product is about twice as much as one just displayed.

Session 5: Menu Options

Preparation: Make a transparency of Activity Master 27. Collect a variety of fraction tools. Provide copies of Activity Masters 15 and 17 (omit zero) to form a game deck for each pair of students. You will need Activity Masters 28 and 29 for Close To and More Than___ But Less Than___. Provide Activity Master 30 for Take Half of What You Spin and About How Many?

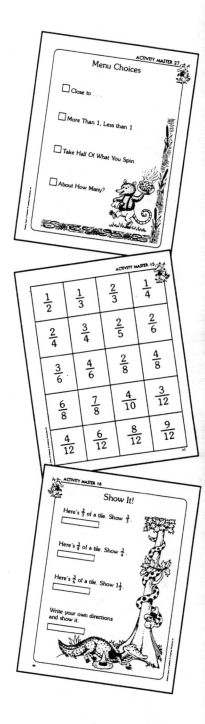

Explain the menu choices and guidelines for completing them.

Menu tasks are designed for partner work.

Allow sufficient time for students to sample all the menu tasks. Provide extra sets of menu materials so groups of students can work on one menu task simultaneously.

Menu Choices

Close To...

Players pick two cards, then estimate whether the product is closest to 0, 1, or 2. They place the cards over that number on the mat. Partners use fraction pieces or a calculator to check. Players keep the cards if they are correct. If not, they forfeit the cards to their partner.

More Than ___ But Less Than ___.

Pick two cards. Estimate and describe the quotient as More Than ___ But Less Than___. Partners must agree or disagree, using fraction pieces or a fraction calculator to check. If correct, keep the cards. If not, forfeit them to your partner.

Take Half of What You Spin and About How Many?

These menu selections provide additional exposure to familiar, "powerful" games. Directions are provided on Activity Master 30.

Session 6: Fraction Problems

Preparation: Provide a variety of fraction tools for students.

Encourage students to create and solve problems.

Problem Task 1:

Boa is close to $10\frac{1}{2}$ feet long. About how old do you think she is if:

- She was $\frac{2}{3}$ foot long at birth.
- She doubled her length the first year.
- She grew about one foot each year after until she was ten.
- Then, she grew only a few inches each year after that.

Boa is between 10 and 11 years old.

Problem Task 2:

According to the local zoo keeper, an alligator's head is about $\frac{1}{3}$ the length of its tail. Its torso is about $\frac{5}{6}$ the length of its tail.

- Gator's tail is about four feet long. How long is Gator? *(Gator is $8\frac{2}{3}$ feet.)*
- If the head length of Gator's friend is about one foot long, how long is her tail? *(3 feet)* What is her entire length? *($6\frac{1}{2}$ feet)*
- Another friend has a head that is about $1\frac{1}{2}$ feet long, how long is her tail? *($4\frac{1}{2}$ feet)* What is her entire length? *($9\frac{3}{4}$ feet)*

Problem Task 3:

The bears set out to pick berries for one of Carol's famous pies. When they stopped picking:

- One bear sampled a berry and then ate $\frac{1}{2}$ of what was left.
- Another bear sampled a berry and ate $\frac{1}{2}$ of what was left.

Maria took the bucket and saw only twelve berries left. How many berries did they pick in all? *(51 berries)*

Making Sense of Fractions © Learning Resources, Inc.

What Was Learned?

Focus on "big ideas" when multiplying and dividing fractions. This will provide further perspectives about students' understandings of fractions.

Examine if students:

- Recognize when it is appropriate to multiply or divide in problem situations.
- Have enough number sense to make good estimations for products and quotients.
- Can determine whether a resulting product or quotient is a reasonable one.

Open-ended tasks like the following address many of these ideas.

Sample Tasks

- $\frac{2}{3}$ of a number is more than one. Using fractions in your response, tell me about the number.

- $1\frac{1}{2}$ times a number is less than one. Tell me about the number.

- When I divide two fractions, the result is between one and two. Tell me about the fractions.

Overall Assessment

Open-ended situations like the following might be posed to provide perspective on students' summate understandings about fractions.

Sample Tasks

Present data such as the following, and ask students to write fraction statements and problems based on the data.

Data for Statements and Problems

Number of Friends	What They Wore
3	Derby hat with pink tie
2	Derby hat with purple tie
1	Derby hat with green tie
6	Helmets with blue plume
6	Helmets with yellow plume
6	Helmets with orange plume
8	Straw hat
2	Baseball cap
2	Ribbons in hair

Making Sense of Fractions © Learning Resources, Inc.

Math and Literature Bibliography

Bradden, Hall, and Taylor. *Math through Children's Literature: Making the NCTM Standards Come Alive.* Englewood, Colorado: Teacher Ideas Press, 1993. ISBN: 0-87287-932-1

Dennis, J. Richard. *Fractions are Parts of Things.* New York: Thomas Y. Crowell Co., 1971. ISBN: 0-690-31520-1

Emberley, Ed. *Picture Pie: A Circle Drawing Book.* Boston: Little, Brown, & Co., 1984. ISBN: 0-316-23425-7

Hutchins, Pat. *The Doorbell Rang.* New York: Greenwillow Books, 1986. ISBN: 0-688-05251-7

Juster, Norton. *The Phantom Tollbooth.* New York: Alfred A. Knopf, 1961. ISBN: 0-394-82037-1

Lease, Lois. *Literature-Based Math, Grades 4-5.* Grand Rapids Michigan: Instructional Fair Inc., 1994. ISBN: 1-56822-165-7

Leedy, Loreen. *Fraction Action.* New York: Holiday House, 1994. ISBN: 0-8234-1109-5

Mathews, Louise. *Gator Pie.* Massachusetts: Sundance Publishing, 1995. ISBN: 0-760-0005-7

McMillan, Bruce. *Eating Fractions.* New York: Scholastic Inc., 1991. ISBN: 0-590-43770-4

Pomerantz, Charlotte. *The Half-Birthday Party.* New York: Ticknor & Fields, 1984. ISBN: 0-89919-273-4

Watson, Clyde. *Tom Fox and the Apple Pie.* New York: Thomas Y. Crowell Co., 1972. ISBN: 0-690-82783-0

ACTIVITY MASTERS

Show and Write Fractions

1. Choose a fraction tool.

2. Pick a fraction from the Fraction Bank.

3. Use a fraction tool to show your fraction.

4. Sketch your fraction and label it.

5. Use other fraction tools to make the same fraction. (Sketch and Label each.)

Repeat this activity with a different fraction from the bank.

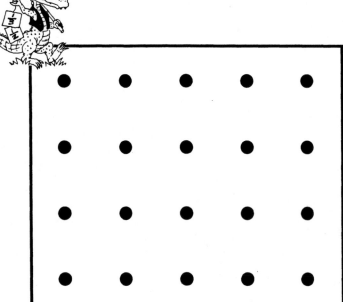

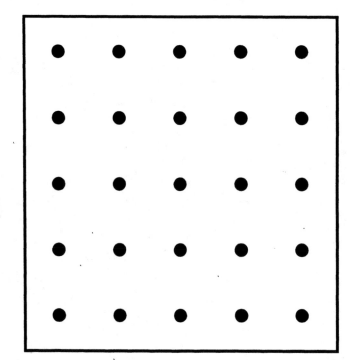

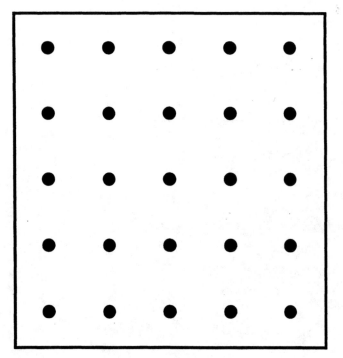

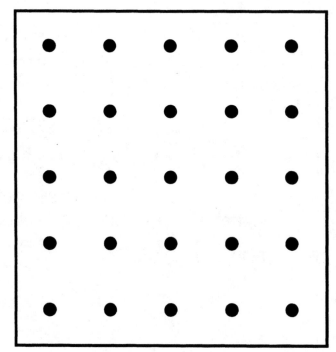

Making Sense of Fractions © Learning Resources, Inc.

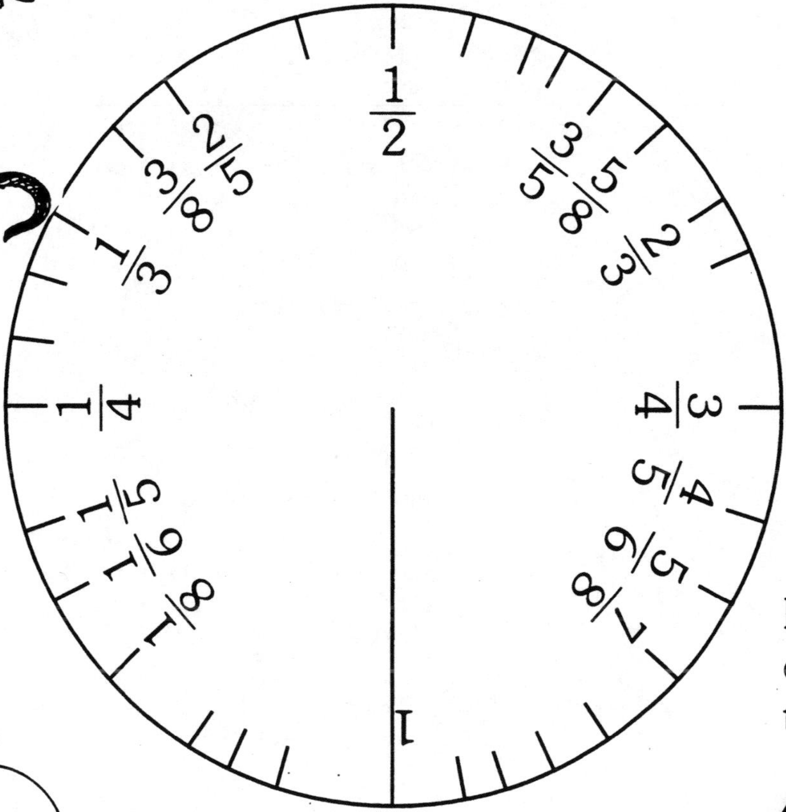
1/2
2/5
3/8
1/3
1/4
1/5
1/6
1/8
3/5
5/8
2/3
3/4
4/5
5/6
7/8
1

Rotate the circles around the center.

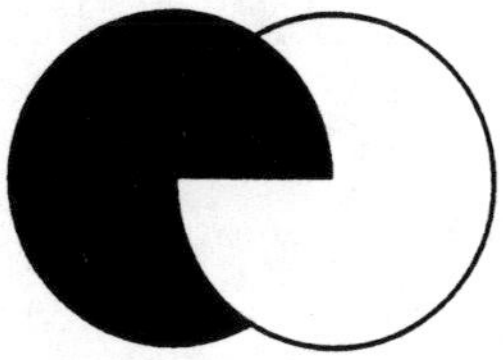

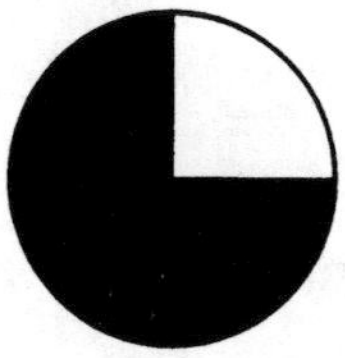

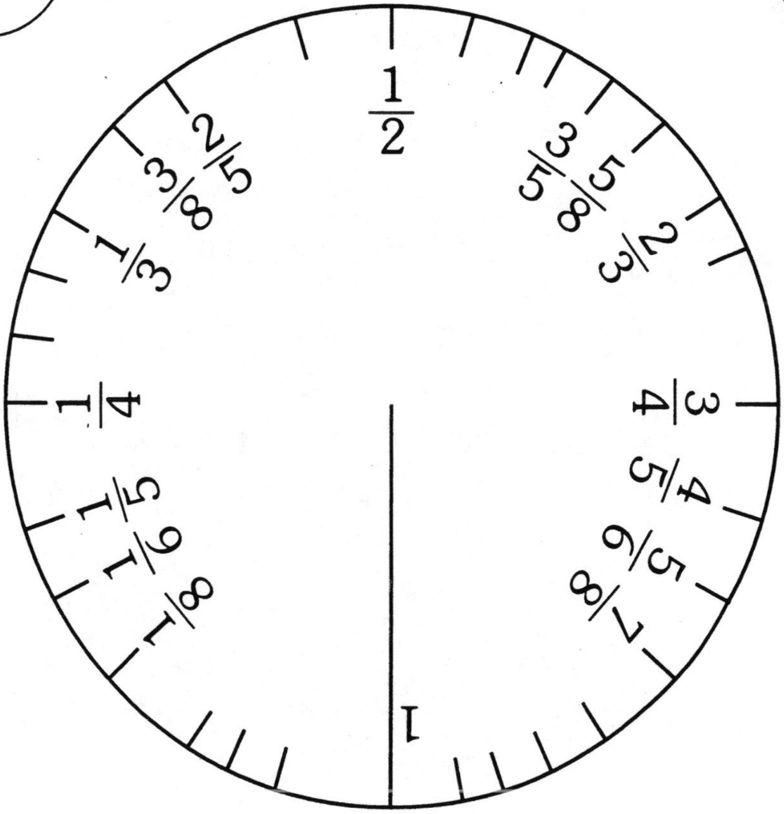
1/2
2/5
3/8
1/3
1/4
1/5
1/6
1/8
3/5
5/8
2/3
3/4
4/5
5/6
7/8
1

Making Sense of Fractions © Learning Resources, Inc.

A

$\frac{1}{8}$ $\frac{1}{16}$ $\frac{1}{4}$ $\frac{1}{2}$ $\frac{1}{8}$ $\frac{1}{16}$

B

$\frac{1}{8}$ $\frac{1}{2}$ $\frac{1}{4}$ $\frac{1}{2}$ $\frac{1}{8}$ $\frac{1}{4}$

Rainbow Fraction Game Mat

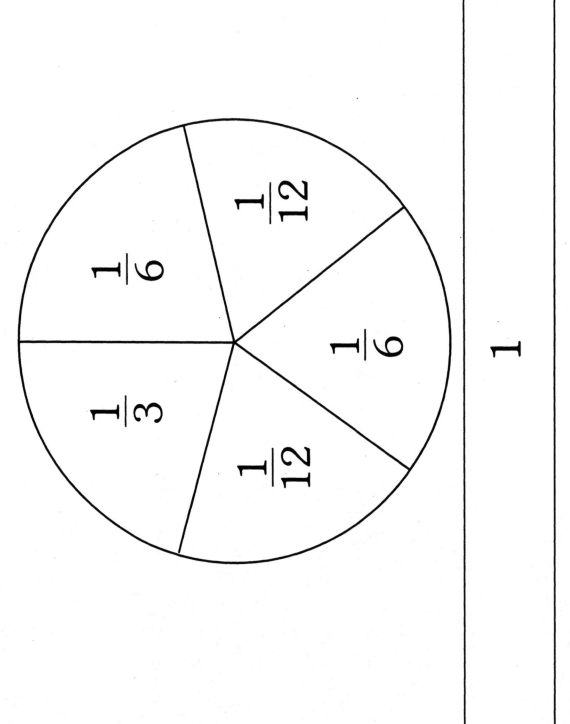

A.

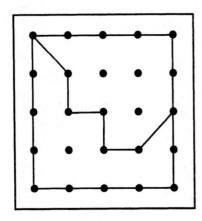

B.

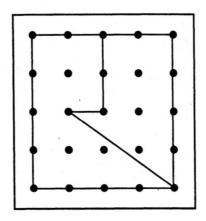

C.

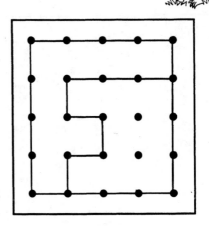

D.

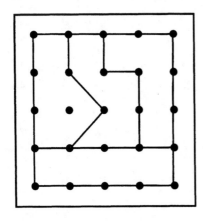

E.

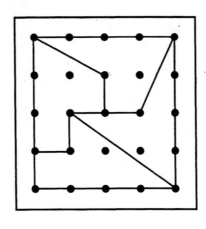

F.

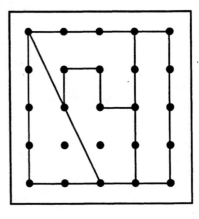

G.

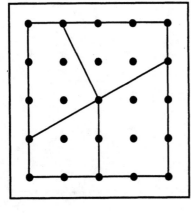

H.

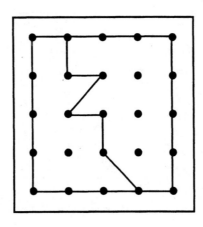

I.

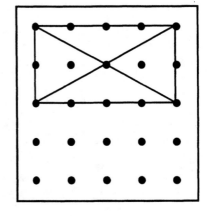

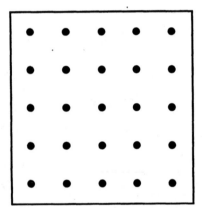
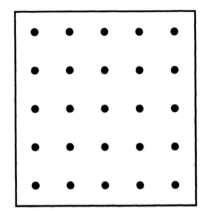
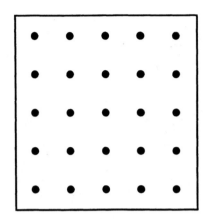

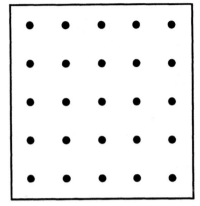
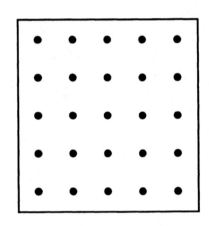
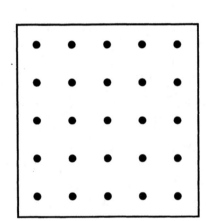

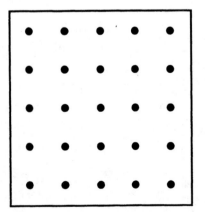
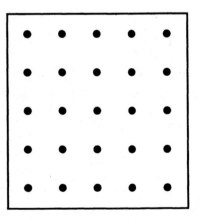
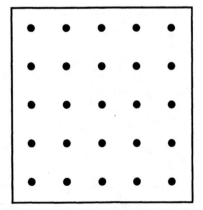

1											

| $\frac{1}{2}$ | | | | | | $\frac{1}{2}$ | | | | | |

| $\frac{1}{3}$ | | | | $\frac{1}{3}$ | | | | $\frac{1}{3}$ | | | |

| $\frac{1}{4}$ | | | $\frac{1}{4}$ | | | $\frac{1}{4}$ | | | $\frac{1}{4}$ | | |

| $\frac{1}{5}$ | | $\frac{1}{5}$ | | $\frac{1}{5}$ | | $\frac{1}{5}$ | | $\frac{1}{5}$ | | | |

| $\frac{1}{6}$ | $\frac{1}{6}$ | $\frac{1}{6}$ | $\frac{1}{6}$ | $\frac{1}{6}$ | $\frac{1}{6}$ | | | | | | |

| $\frac{1}{8}$ | $\frac{1}{8}$ | $\frac{1}{8}$ | $\frac{1}{8}$ | $\frac{1}{8}$ | $\frac{1}{8}$ | $\frac{1}{8}$ | $\frac{1}{8}$ | | | | |

| $\frac{1}{10}$ | $\frac{1}{10}$ | $\frac{1}{10}$ | $\frac{1}{10}$ | $\frac{1}{10}$ | $\frac{1}{10}$ | $\frac{1}{10}$ | $\frac{1}{10}$ | $\frac{1}{10}$ | $\frac{1}{10}$ | | |

| $\frac{1}{12}$ | $\frac{1}{12}$ | $\frac{1}{12}$ | $\frac{1}{12}$ | $\frac{1}{12}$ | $\frac{1}{12}$ | $\frac{1}{12}$ | $\frac{1}{12}$ | $\frac{1}{12}$ | $\frac{1}{12}$ | $\frac{1}{12}$ | $\frac{1}{12}$ |

More ~ Less ~ Equal

1. Choose a fraction tool.

2. Demonstrate two fractions with the tool.

3. Make statements to compare fractions or show equivalence. See how many different statements you can make.

4. Draw a sketch and label it.

Repeat the steps for other fractions.

$\frac{1}{2}$	$\frac{1}{3}$	$\frac{2}{3}$	$\frac{1}{4}$
$\frac{2}{4}$	$\frac{3}{4}$	$\frac{2}{5}$	$\frac{2}{6}$
$\frac{3}{6}$	$\frac{4}{6}$	$\frac{2}{8}$	$\frac{4}{8}$
$\frac{6}{8}$	$\frac{7}{8}$	$\frac{4}{10}$	$\frac{3}{12}$
$\frac{4}{12}$	$\frac{6}{12}$	$\frac{8}{12}$	$\frac{9}{12}$

Which is Less? ~ Which is More?

Mix the cards and put them face down in a pile.

1. Each player picks one fraction card.

2. If equivalent fractions are drawn, players keep their card.

3. Spin the spinner. Make a statement about the two fractions using the word from the spinner.

4. The spinner determines who takes both cards — the one with the lesser or greater fraction.

Continue until all cards are gone. Spin one more time. The player who has more or less cards according to the spinner is the winner!

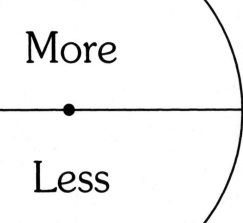

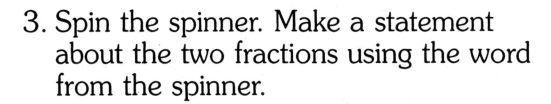

Making Sense of Fractions © Learning Resources, Inc.

$\frac{0}{2}$	$\frac{2}{2}$	$\frac{4}{4}$	$1\frac{1}{2}$
$\frac{3}{2}$	$1\frac{3}{4}$	$\frac{7}{4}$	$\frac{16}{8}$
$2\frac{1}{2}$	$\frac{5}{2}$	$2\frac{5}{8}$	$\frac{21}{8}$
$3\frac{1}{4}$	$\frac{13}{4}$	$3\frac{1}{2}$	0
1	2	3	4

Show It!

Here's $\frac{2}{3}$ of a tile. Show $\frac{3}{3}$.

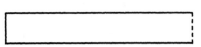

Here's $\frac{3}{8}$ of a tile. Show $\frac{3}{4}$.

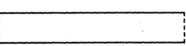

Here's $\frac{3}{6}$ of a tile. Show $1\frac{1}{3}$.

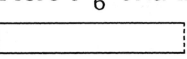

Write your own directions
and show it.

Making Sense of Fractions © Learning Resources, Inc.

Pizza Pieces

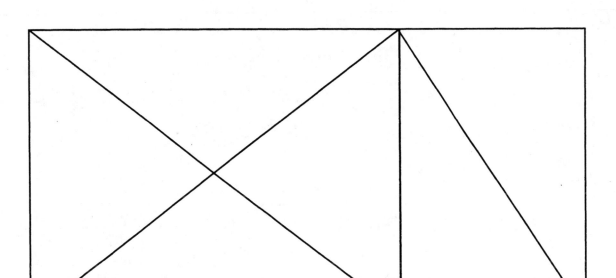

Alicia cut six pizza pieces as shown. Alfredo did not think they were all the same size. Alicia disagreed. Write what you think.

Explain your reasoning.

_____

_____

_____

_____

_____

Pizza Problems

Derek and Kenji ordered two large pizzas. Derek ate $\frac{6}{8}$ of his pizza. Kenji ate $\frac{4}{6}$ of his pizza. Derek said they both ate the same amount because each had two pieces left.
Kenji disagreed.

Write what you think.

Explain your reasoning.

- -

There was $\frac{1}{3}$ of a pizza left.
Beth ate $\frac{1}{2}$ of what was left.
Then, Tina ate $\frac{1}{2}$ of what Beth left.

What fractional part of the pizza did Beth eat? Tina eat?

Who ate the bigger piece of the left-over pizza?

What part of the pizza was left after Tina ate her piece?

What You Spin Is What You Take

1. Spin to see who goes first.

2. Spin and place the matching fraction piece on the whole.

3. Keep a running total of what is on your mat.

4. If a player spins and lands on a piece that is too big to fit on their mat, go to the next player.

The winner is the first to make exactly one whole!

What You Spin Is What You Take Away

1. Spin to see who goes first.

2. Start with the whole piece.

3. Spin and take the matching fraction piece away, making trades as needed.

4. If there is not enough to take what is on the spinner, the next player gets a turn.

5. Keep track of what is on your mat.

The winner is the first to remove all fraction pieces!

Menu Choices

☐ Close to . . .

☐ Two and Two

☐ Pick 4

☐ What You Spin Is What You Take

☐ What You Spin Is What You Take Away

Close To . . .

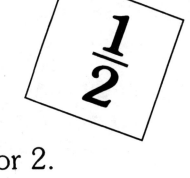

$\frac{1}{2}$

1. Player picks 2 cards,
   then estimates whether the
   sum is closer to 0, $\frac{1}{2}$, 1, $1\frac{1}{2}$, or 2.

2. Place the cards over that number.

3. Partner agrees or disagrees
   using fraction pieces or a fraction
   calculator to check.

1

4. Player keeps the cards if he/she is
   correct. If not, forfeit the cards to
   your partner.

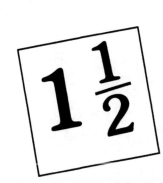

$1\frac{1}{2}$

2

Two and Two

1. Each player picks two cards. Alternate adding and subtracting fractions in each round. Add in the first round. Subtract in the next.

2. Record the results.

3. On the <u>subtraction</u> round, the player with the smaller result tallies 1 point.

4. On the <u>addition</u> round, the player with the greater result tallies 1 point.

5. Use fraction tools to help or check.

Game ends at 10 points.

Pick 4

1. Draw 4 cards. Use as many as needed to show a sum that is <u>greater</u> <u>than</u> $\frac{1}{2}$ but <u>less</u> <u>than</u> $1\frac{1}{2}$.

2. Record your answer.

3. Use fraction tools to help or check.

4. Repeat using different cards.

What's The Problem?

1. Secretly pick two fractions and add or subtract them.

2. Tell your partner the answer.

3. Your partner tells you what the problem could have been!

- -

Pick and Place

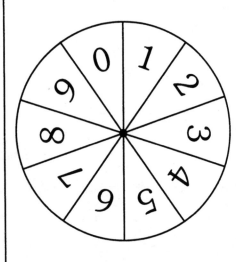

1. Copy the fraction mat on paper.

2. Spin and write the number on your mat.

3. Repeat. Arrange the numbers to fit the box below.

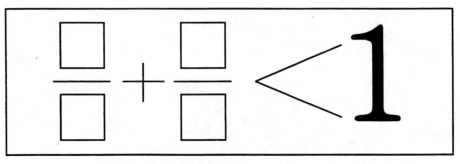

Fraction Mat

Making Sense of Fractions © Learning Resources, Inc.

Menu Choices

☐ Close to . . .

☐ More Than 1, Less than 1

☐ Take Half Of What You Spin

☐ About How Many?

Close To . . .

0

1. Players pick two cards, then estimate whether the product is closer to 0, $\frac{1}{2}$, 1, $1\frac{1}{2}$, or 2.

2. Place the cards over that number on the mat.

3. Partner agrees or disagrees using fraction pieces or a fraction calculator to check.

1

2

4. Keep the cards if correct. If not, forfeit the cards to your partner.

Making Sense of Fractions © Learning Resources. Inc.

More Than___, But Less Than___

In turn:

1. Pick 2 cards.

2. Estimate and describe the quotient
   as "more than ___, but less than ___."

3. Partner agrees or disagrees.

4. If correct, keep the cards.
   If not, forfeit them to partner.

Continue until all the cards are played.

Take Half of What You Spin

1. Spin to see who goes first.

2. Spin and place the piece for <u>half</u> of what the spinner says.

3. Record.

4. If there is not enough room to place a piece, the next player has a turn.

- -

About How Many?

1. Spin to see who goes first.

2. Fill the mat part way.

3. Spin and tell about how many fraction pieces (for the spinner number) would exactly cover what is on the mat.

4. Record to describe.

5. Tally one point if your partner agrees.